COUNTRY MATT[ERS]

PUNCH'S

Rural Retreats

Edited by William Hewison

A PUNCH BOOK

Published in Association with Grafton
An Imprint of HarperCollins*Publishers*

Grafton
An Imprint of HarperCollins*Publishers*
77–85 Fulham Palace Road
Hammersmith, London W6 8JB

Published by Grafton 1991
1 3 5 7 9 10 8 6 4 2

Copyright © Punch Publications Limited 1991

A catalogue record for this book
is available from the British Library

ISBN 0-586-21482-8

Printed in Great Britain by
Mackays of Chatham plc, Chatham, Kent

Introduction

Ever thought about the *mechanics* of a cartoon? By that I mean the way it is put together in order to achieve its function? It's a tricky area to get into because before you know it you are rubbing up against that intractable 'What is Humour?' thing. Many great minds have stumbled over that one, going all high-falutin' and philosophical. A far easier task is to calculate how many angels can dance on the head of a pin. (Here I cannot resist recalling a substantial essay on Humour by Arthur Koestler wherein he came an almighty cropper when his intellectual analysis of a particular cartoon from *The New Yorker* showed that he had missed its real point completely.)

The simplest definition of a cartoon is that it is a riddle. It is not a complete statement like 'The cat sat on the mat'. What the cartoonist does is to provide various bits of information but cunningly to leave a gap which the reader is expected to fill himself. A cartoon is a collaboration. If the reader is incapable of supplying the missing piece – his general knowledge may be limited or he might not be very bright – then he doesn't get the joke. Mind you, occasionally the cartoonist tries to be too clever with his riddle and the point is lost for a great many people.

Ideas come to cartoonists sometimes in a flash of inspiration but more normally they are the result of hard think-sessions. Once the idea is honed to the required sharpness it has to be organized into a cartoon by way of a well-plotted drawing and a carefully worded caption (with, remember, one important piece missing) so that when the reader 'solves the riddle' a sudden burst of surprise and amusement is experienced. Is this getting too fanciful? I hope not. You will find a fair example of this mechanism at work in the Starke drawing captioned 'I'm afraid it is necessary to ask each of you ladies a personal question'.

With the added observation that cartoons cover a wide spectrum of humour (from surreal zany to homely recognition) I'd better leave this exposition there, before I do a Koestler.

Now this particular collection of *Punch* cartoons

is concerned with all things rustic. From my personal knowledge of the people who produced them, I'd say that fields and hedgerows are not their normal habitat; green wellies, pink hunting coats and the 12-bore at the shoulder – these seem not to feature prominently in their day-to-day activities. No, as in all other cartoon subjects the material for this book comes from suburbanites with a jackdaw capacity for collecting masses of extraneous facts – and it is from this extravagant compost that they propagate their comical ideas.

However, there is one cartoonist, an ex-Birkenheadian, who has been a *bona fide* country dweller for a good many years: Norman Thelwell. So it is not surprising that he has been the one who first recorded (through cartoons the trade calls 'social comment') rural developments like factory farming, hen batteries, agribusiness, the hunt protesters, buyers of weekend cottages, the junk motor cars abandoned in the hedgerows. And a regular target: the ever grumbling farmer. (Yes, I know Thelwell is famous for his fat gymkhana ponies – those were for the kiddie-winkies – but you'll find none of them here.)

Once established these subjects became source material for the rest of the cartoon gang, who also held on to elements of an older more picturesque order. Nowadays do you see a scarecrow anywhere but in a cartoon?

William Hewison

"Oh good, here he comes to sell us eggs and butter and that sort of thing."

"I do hope this is undiscovered and not passé."

"Progress, they call it – and the countryside be damned."

"I know what makes it seem unnatural – no background music."

"My God, who left that gate open? They've gone completely berserk!"

"Oh Jethro! He touched his forelock for the first time today!"

"You jump about and then they notice you and then they eat you."

*"Who the hell do you **think** they belong to – who else but those blasted demonstrators!"*

"It's come several weeks too early – I hadn't finished complaining about the drought."

"Do let's buy it, Geoffrey."

"Just ignore it. It's another local smart alec."

*"I'll never have the guts to tell her, of course, but **I adored** the rat race!"*

"Up here it's just us and the model aeroplanes."

"I have to inform you that you have been sent to Coventry."

"The rather long, thin bill and high forehead are distinctive, as is the flight, which makes a high whirring sound. And for the true gastronome nothing can rival it roasted in brandy."

"Must beat the locals at their own game, Hiram – so on with the stetson, the cameras, the ol' Texas drawl – and don't forget to get whitewashed at darts."

"OK – your lap again."

"Hello! The death duties have been paid off."

HARGREAVES

"I hate to say it, but they make a colourful sight."

"Whatever it is, it's gone up that tree."

"If there's one thing I hate about a meet . . ."

". . . so what with the difficulty of finding decent gardening staff, paving slabs seemed to be the sensible solution."

"Damned weather! All right, Withers, start beating."

*"Of course their intelligence is
carefully bred out of them . . ."*

"Crash! Wallop! Bang! Every time we get a bit of fog."

"We'll give it another five minutes."

"Let's enjoy it while we can – this is where they're going to build the new Leisure Centre."

"We've gone back to the Three-Field System – one belongs to an Arab, one to a Dutchman and one to a pension fund."

"I see they've tarted up all the pubs in this area."

"I told you not to build it in the orchard."

". . . and then, before you know it, it's Motorway Inquiry time again."

"Those were the days – 'Here a cluck. There a cluck. Everywhere a cluck-cluck'."

"To have any effect I find I have to make it more scary every year."

"For God's sake, Colonel! Cut out the 'Dance, dance' bit – here's the Anti-Blood Sports League."

"Not very quick, is it?"

"This is one of the few places still left that hasn't come out in paperback."

"Strawberry mousse! Strawberry mousse!"

"I'm afraid it is necessary to ask each of you ladies a personal question."

"Open the window, Frisby, and shout yoo-hoo."

"Two ploughman's, four fireman's, four binman's, three businessman's, two policeman's . . ."

"Apparently we're now on the old road taken by the original tourists."

*"Come out of there, Freddie – you don't know **what** it's been sprayed with."*

"Never mind the delay – you've got your car cleaned."

"I'll be glad when we're safely through the Green Belt."

"This is just a little experiment we're conducting."

"It's from the council, Fiona – they've refused us permission to build an outside privy."

"Beats me how they got planning permission."

"What's a neighbour?"

*"What do you mean, you don't want it?
With a little practice this could give you
a lifetime's smoked salmon sandwiches."*

*"Sometimes I think you're not really **trying**."*

"Electricity, fast trains, main drainage – are you trying to ruin the amenities of the village?"

"Gentleman from the council to see you, Fred – shall I let him into the library?"

"Pretty, be damned – it's a bird of ill-omen."

"We're having trouble with foxes."

"The slugs are a bloody nuisance as well."

"Mr Macdonald?"

"I think that completes our little flock."

"Free range is all very well but I do miss my early morning call."

"They're back."

"I understand it's intended as a compliment."

"Welcome to the colony. That's odd – we always thought that **you** *were* **Mr** *Brewster and that* **you** *were* **Mrs** *Brewster!"*

"Apparently, this hill is interesting in that it has no associations with Thomas Hardy."

"The Pennine Way just isn't the same these days!"

"Hey! Was that you – clowning around with that bird-call thing?"

". . . having chosen your breathtaking view, you are now ready to set up your easel, arrange your paint tubes and select your brushes in preparation for painting your Willoughby Scenic Tour No. 207 masterpiece."

*"This is nearly perfect; if **only** it could be on my expense account."*

"I think they're waiting for us to dance."

"I sometimes wonder what they do with it all."

"If the floods go on subsiding at this rate we'll be faced by a serious drought."

*"If mist there be o'er Gurlford Peak,
'Tis plastic macs for rest of week."*

"There's two tons of cattle cake to come yet."

*"**And** I'd just bought 'Welsh For Beginners'."*

*"**Here** I am, Dominic!"*

"Wait, Dad – I've won the pig!"

"No, don't tell me . . ."

"You've had all winter to get ready."

"Last one home polishes the cups."

HARGREAVES

"On the contrary. I feel that I'm an excellent snowman. It's just that I arrived on the scene at an unfortunate time."

"Why can't you keep them in a nice warm battery house, or something?"

"We get up at six o'clock every morning to milk the EEC agricultural subsidies."

"Pow!"

"I've got a three litre Rover at the moment – about a mile outside Salford."

*"You never hear anything about testing **their** breath."*

"Isn't it maddening!"

"Now why don't you go out there? You're supposed to be a free ranger."

"Perkins, this place is like a pigsty."

*"**Please**, Freddie! It somehow gives me the creeps."*

"Head for the hills – we've been voted the Prettiest Village in Britain!"

"What do you know, he's made of plastic."

"There's 5000 acres of arable, with Elizabethan farmhouse and cottages, but it's well below your price range."

"Yes sir, I just took a fox to the fifth floor!"

HARGREAVES.

"That's funny! The guide book definitely speaks of a secluded pool."

"There's a space, Dad!"

*"I understand it's already been twinned with an area ripe for
development in France."*

"Now there's a chap that can put them up."

"I love it! The excitement, the smell of aniseed, the occasional punch-up."

". . . and there'll be a herd of cattle somewhere with our groceries."

"I've always envied their irresistible urge to be on the move."

"My goodness – is that the time?"

"Disgraceful – what's the County Council doing, I'd like to know!"

"Well, hurry it up – couldn't you have thought of something to yell beforehand?"

"We won't learn much from this lot. They haven't got around to the wheel yet."